THREAD RIPPER

THREAD RIPPER
Amalie Smith

Translated by
Jennifer Russell

Lolli Editions
London

NOTES

.TXT

1

PART 1 | THE WAVERING PENELOPE

3   While Odysseus is away on his long journey, Penelope
weaves. Her loom, I imagine, stands by the window.
On the road outside stand her 108 suitors. Penelope
leans out.

'Suitors,' she says, 'let us make an agreement.
I am weaving a burial shroud for my father-in-law,
Laertes. Not until I have finished this shroud will
I remarry.'

The suitors accept and retreat from her window.
Penelope continues her work at the loom. During the
day, she stands by the window — weaving as agreed —
but at night she returns and unravels the day's work.

Alone in the cabin in the woods.

A long, vivid dream about a singer last night;
we shared a kiss and a common future.

Stayed in bed for a long time, didn't want
to wake up.

Such wonderful weeks with William, thought
about having a baby instead of a dog or a cat
like we've talked about.

Now a longing for something else burns inside me.

Once she has finished her unravelling, she falls asleep in the bed Odysseus carved from a rooted tree. It cannot be moved.

Penelope weaves on a warp-weighted loom, one of the oldest types. Its warp threads are suspended from a crossbeam and held taut by weights tied to the ends. The loom leans against a wall, and the weaver works standing upright.

What is Penelope weaving? It never comes together to form an image.

4

Penelope by day: assembling an image. Penelope by night: dismantling an image into its physical components.

I am Penelope, but not the faithful wife. I weave and unravel a tapestry while I long and waver.

Restless heart.

Left the cabin Monday and returned yesterday
— a season has gone by in the meantime.

The green and wet of summer, the dusty light
of autumn. Then, unmoving air. Now, strong winds.

In the garden, I can hear a gust five or six
seconds before it whips through my books on
the table.

5

Lonesome life, what is it I want?

To take the best of my twenties into my thirties?
Courage? Naivety?

I have come to the cabin in the woods to take
pictures of plants and work on the tapestry.

Last year, Mary showed me a path through the
hills and down to the coast.

I am trained as a tapestry-weaver. My schooling
promised me that subject matter and material are
two sides of the same coin. That any decision
can be put off until the moment I've got the material
in my hands.

The tapestry is a commission. It will hang in the
entrance hall of the Agency for Digitisation.
Which makes me a state-employed tapestry weaver
for the coming year.

5

I am weaving a tapestry — or rather, I am designing
a tapestry on my computer screen; afterwards
it will be woven on an industrial digital loom.

I have built this computer myself. I chose a processor
with eight cores and 16 threads, an AMD Ryzen
Threadripper. I tore its label in half and named the
computer Thread Ripper.

Down by the creek, she picked a horsetail and
said, 'This is one of the first plants that grew
on Earth.'

The shape of the prehistoric plant: a green
segmented stem wreathed by wiry, leafless tubes.

When we emerged from the juniper thicket
to a view of a wheatfield, she exclaimed,
'A biological wasteland!'

Now I carry both sentences with me as I walk
the same route on my own.

6

Regarding the dream still simmering inside me:
I need more time.

But biology is not (yet) negotiable. My eggs are
running out.

I told William on the phone, 'I need to finish
the tapestry before I know what I want.'

I am the wavering Penelope.

It is Thread Ripper that gathers the threads and Thread Ripper that rips them apart. By threads I mean rays. By rays I mean textile.

The loom is an ancient technology, possibly the very oldest. Archaeological findings date the loom back to 5,000 BC, making it a predecessor to both mathematics and writing. Weaving an image, unlike drawing with your finger in the sand, requires planning and logical thinking.

On the loom, the abstract becomes concrete, because a textile is produced, and the concrete abstract, as an image is formed.

The phone is an escape from the cabin and the landscape, but what kind of escape?

A single hair vibrates on the banks of a brook. A thicket stands guard around a forest, making it dense like a loaf of bread.

A red cow's tongue stretches out and ropes in the long grass so its teeth can catch hold.

Unnerving to look at the cows and not recognise them as anything but animals for slaughter. To see their hides stretched out and tacked to a wall, their tongues packaged in the supermarket fridge.

To see them as robots — a mass of dead elements assembled for motion.

At the window: a spider opens a hatch to its wrapped-up prey and sucks the nutrients from its insides.

There's nourishment in everything, it tells me.

A Brazilian violet has underground leaves that catch and eat worms!

I am weaving a tapestry for the Agency for
Digitisation because the first computer was a loom.
Weavers were the first programmers, and textile
the fabric of the digital.

When the merchant Joseph Marie Jacquard uses
punched cards to automate the loom in the early
1800s, it becomes possible to streamline the
production of patterned textiles. The punched cards
store textile patterns the same way the studded
tin of a music box stores a melody.

Together with the steam engine, this invention fuels
the industrialisation of France. Thousands of dexterous
weavers can be replaced by perforated paper cards
and steam.

The prehistoric plants now pumped from the ground as oil once filled the atmosphere with so much oxygen insects grew as big as birds.

Atoms vibrate, molecules revolve and combine and divide; cries and voices propagate through the air.

If only you could inhabit the air and absorb nutrients from intonation and breath.

Convert the sun's rays into blood sugar.

I need to stop drooling over the singer on YouTube like a damn teenager.

Why this sense of fatedness, as if everything he sings were addressed to me?

As if he could touch the place inside of me that's alive.

But he can.

In the United Kingdom too, industrialisation is picking up speed. Here, in the 1830s, it occurs to mathematician Charles Babbage that Jacquard's punched cards might be used to store much more than weaving patterns. He devises the Analytical Engine, a steam-powered, 14-metre-long mechanical calculator which uses the loom's punched cards to store data and operating algorithms. Although it was never built, it is considered the world's first computer.

Countess Ada Lovelace, a friend of Charles Babbage, studies mathematics and writes notes to accompany his invention. Daughter of poet Lord Byron, she shows an eye for the poetic correlation between the machine and the loom, and writes:

'We may say most aptly that the Analytical Engine weaves algebraic patterns just as the Jacquard-loom weaves flowers and leaves.'

This infatuation like having your cover flung open, a heavy slumber, like riding, letting yourself be led, getting carried away.

Not being sure of the story of the universe's infiniteness.

Reading a text backwards on a pane of glass.

This living hand that writes.   9

Or that which lives in the 3D-modelled landscapes of the desert.

Or that which is carried by the air.

Or that which is woven forth in the pixel tapestries of computer screens, zeroes and ones.

Or that which eats until full and seals itself off, dissolves, hardens into a new form, unfurls a pair of wide, image-adorned wings and lets them dry in the sun.

The punched card is the physical link connecting the history of the computer to that of the loom. If we trace this connection backwards, we see that the history of the computer extends thousands of years.

With the invention of weaving, humans have already broken down images into points that are assembled into chains, in turn assembled into a pattern or image, not unlike pixels on a screen.

Jacquard could apply punched cards to the loom because weaving is intrinsically a binary technology: the weft is passed over or under the warp. These two possibilities permitted translation into hole or no-hole in the punched card. And later, into zeroes and ones.

9

What does the butterfly know of the images on its wings?

It knows what it means to be an image from the inside out, with no regard for the outside in.

What can we know of the butterfly's images when we are only able to *see* them?

Therapy 14/9: it isn't about the singer. It's me who could become more: unfiltered, sensitive, free of shame, in touch.   10

I am allowed to: dream big, reach out, receive, cooperate, believe in something, have an impact, make myself heard, make a decision, step forward, become clear.

Stayed up all night uploading and downloading my plant pictures to the algorithm via an internet connection shared from my phone.

A committee at the Agency for Digitisation has approved the tapestry's design even though I have yet to show them a single picture of what it will look like.

I told them about the loom and the punched card, and how I plan to create the imagery.

I intend to take pictures of plants and feed them to a machine-learning algorithm, which will then generate images of new digital vegetation based on the images I feed it.

10

Working together with the machine-learning algorithm, I will weave and unravel artificial plant images on screen. A *Flora digitalica*, I told the committee.

I was born into the then-growing middle class of 1980s Copenhagen. An exceptional time, as it turns out. I am the same age as the internet.

At five o'clock, a car pulled all the way up to the cabin, a door slammed.

Half an hour later, shots sounded from the woods.

How thin-skinned I looked in the mirror after an entire night without sleep.

Three or four yellow pimples on chapped skin covered in an oil film.

If only my face would fade or get worn out so I could have a new one.

A face more courageous, more capable, more lit up from within, solid, baked, hard and beautiful.

Invincible like a young man who has never been sick, has never got down on his knees or asked anyone for anything.

William was here. Two nights in the cabin, two days, a weekend.

My mother studied maths and worked as a high
school teacher. She gave me my first computer
when I turned 12, and ever since I have woven pixel
tapestries on ever flatter and brighter screens.

My father trained as a psychotherapist in the early
1990s. One day he told me, 'I have a hard time
placing you in any category or theory. Each time
I think I've managed, you elude it.'

I adopted this elusiveness as a badge of honour.
I evolve. I wriggle my way out. I am sceptical of all
that is static.

11

I am Penelope, but not the faithful wife. I am the
wavering Penelope. I weave a fabric of dreams
and unravel it, weave another and unravel that, so
creating an endlessly unfinished image.

He brought me a book of Maria Sibylla
Merian's illustrated metamorphosis plates.

The voices of children in the forest stretched
like rubber bands towards a black September sky.

The moon made the clouds white and distant
like Pixar animations, completely crisp.

William had to go inside and fetch his glasses
to see them.

The fear that arises when you care about
something is the fear of loss.

Bresson writes: 'The omnipotence of rhythms.
Nothing is durable but what is caught up in
rhythms.'

When William is here, I can read but not write.

Is nature void of windows or screens that open
up to alternate realities?

The threads create a flat image within which the eye opens up a space that collapses back into two dimensions and unravels into threads.

The cocoon of a silk moth consists of a single, unbroken thread, which may be extracted and woven into a durable textile.

For at least 3,000 years, silk production is kept a Chinese secret. In the fourth century, a Japanese expedition kidnaps four Chinese girls and a handful of eggs and forces the girls to teach them the craft.

A mushroom kicked partially to pieces.
A steel-blue beetle in the grass.

Rising in black discs from the trail of the forest
floor, the far too shallow root system of fallen
birch trees.

The soil is so wet it isn't worth their while to
send their roots deeper.

13

I stood watching the soft, free swinging of the
cows' tails and was reminded of dancers letting
their bodies drop limply to the floor.

The shadow of a cloud slid across the meadow,
came towards me, engulfed me.

Cows are slow creatures who keep busy eating.

Manmade animals. We have taken the laziest,
hungriest specimens and bred them *ad absurdum*.

In the sixth century, two Christian monks successfully smuggle silkworm eggs concealed in their bamboo canes back to the Byzantine emperor, who starts his own silk monopoly. Only after the crusades of the Middle Ages is the metamorphosis of silkworms established as a proper industry in Europe.

Maria Sibylla Merian grows up in Frankfurt in the mid-1600s, the daughter of a publisher and stepdaughter of a flower painter.

At the age of 13, she spends all her free time studying insects. She collects moths and butterflies in and around Frankfurt and raises them in her family's home. She obtains silkworm eggs from silk mills in the city and studies their development from egg to larva to cocoon to white-furred silk moth. She feeds the larvae fresh mulberry leaves.

A cow calls for the others at shorter and
shorter intervals, but no one reacts.

Darkness falls. A bird shrieks in the woods.
The cows lift their heads. Infinitely slowly.

If there existed a device for recording smells,
I would send William the hot, yeasty breath
of a ruminating cow.

14

Down the gravel road is a rail house that
no longer belongs to anyone.

You can yearn beyond the hills, but can
you cut that yearning and put it in water
like a bouquet of wildflowers?

Today on the bridge that leads across the creek,
the black earth mottled with yellow birch leaves.

In Merian's time, most people believe that life emerges from non-living matter through 'spontaneous generation'. Maggots are thought to come from dead flesh, while mice supposedly arise from piles of old rags.

In detailed watercolours and hand-painted copperplate engravings, Merian illustrates the metamorphoses of insects on their natural host plants. Her plates are considered among the very first illustrations of ecosystems.

I imagine Merian in her room, opening the box of silkworms, finding that today they have formed big, velvety cocoons. She wets her brush and ponders how to capture in watercolour this white and airy structure.

First rain, then sun. The air glistens with rays.

A spider's web across the path, and when my
hand hits it, the same staticky sound as touching
a satin pillow.

The world is created again and again.

Beginners everywhere.

The fog across the meadow lifts, forming
a cast of the landscape.   15

Then a wind takes hold, a faint and imperceptible
breeze that pulls the fog out of shape.

Soon the sun will be hot enough to make the
white evaporate and retreat into the sky.

In the time I have been here, the view from my
window has yellowed in a long, soundless sigh.

At the end of the 1700s, a new type of moth arrives in Europe from Asia. These are not reared in incubation boxes, but thrive in their damp, stove-heated homes. They are golden-brown and smaller than the silk moth. Their habitat is the wardrobe.

After fertilisation, the female lays eggs in wool clothing and silk, and from the eggs hatch larvae that unravel the textiles and spin them into new structures.

15

The clothes moth threatens the bonds that hold textiles together.

No, the trees most likely do not feel. They act, they decide, but they do not harbour nostalgia or longing.

Or, if they do: poor things.

16

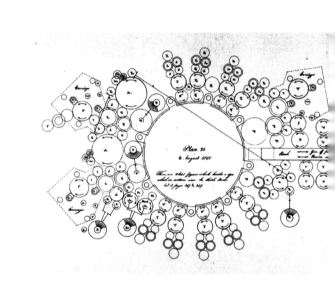

Plan 26
6. August 1840

17

PART 2 | ADA'S ALGORITHM

When Ada Lovelace meets Charles Babbage in 1833,
he has already constructed his first mechanical
calculator, the Difference Engine, and is now planning
an improved version that functions in cycles.
'A locomotive that lays down its own railway,'
he calls it. 'An engine eating its own tail.'

Ada is 17, Charles 41, and the two strike up an
unusual friendship. Charles shares with Ada the
plans for what will become the Analytical Engine.

B — OCTOBER 2017

When autumn said, 'Autumn,' I was ready for
the adventures of summer.

Back in the city. When I opened my duffel bag
to unpack after the week in the woods, a moth
fluttered up into the air.

Over the course of the next ten years — during which she marries William King, gives birth to three children and becomes the Countess of Lovelace — Ada studies analytical mathematics via correspondence. She grasps not only the principles of the Analytical Engine but also its potential, which makes her eager to realise the machine.

Charles runs foul of his investors, and to help him convince the world of the invention's importance, Ada translates a lecture he gave in Turin from French to English.

19

She finds it inadequate and adds her own supplementary remarks, a translator's note of sorts. This engine, she asserts, would prompt the development of a whole new language, which could be used for much more than mathematical calculations. Not only would it be able to process numbers, but also, in principle, letters or even music.

Anything that can be converted into data.

Autumn air, fat like a pregnancy.

Don't poke me in the belly about my
childlessness.

Give me a fish to cradle, a kitten, a lamb,
a cow pie.

I hear on the radio that the human brain at
birth is a soup of connections, that language
helps us reduce them.

The more we learn, the fewer the connections.

I read more and more about Ada.

Although she lived in another time, I can't help
but see myself in her.

Her husband's name was William. Her mother
was a mathematician. Her father worked with
emotions.

I imagine Ada at her desk in the cool summer of 1843. The drapes are drawn in her study: she is completely engrossed in her notes. She doesn't sleep, doesn't eat, devotes all her energy to uncovering what a mechanical calculator might accomplish in the world.

In pencil, she writes: 'In enabling mechanism to combine together general symbols in successions of unlimited variety and extent, a uniting link is established between the operations of matter and the abstract mental processes of the most abstract branch of mathematical science.'

I imagine it is this 'uniting link' that drives her.

20

Her notes grow to double the length of Charles's lecture. Although she has given birth to three children, she calls this work her firstborn.

William assists at the birth, writing up her notes in ink. Ada signs them A. A. L: Augusta Ada Lovelace.

She needed more time.

I read a book about why the computer was
not invented in antiquity.

First, the spirits had to be expelled from nature.

Then, the world had to be perceived as a perfect
clockwork created by one almighty God.

Only after that could humans begin to view
themselves as machines.

Only then could people imagine constructing
a mechanical brain.

And after that, the mechanical nervous system.

The digital has become a source not of order,
as we had hoped, but of mess, an accumulation
of images and signs that just keeps on growing.

Her notes are labelled A–G. In note G she details how
the engine could use recursive cycles to compute a
sequence known as the Bernoulli numbers. This work
of hers is today considered the world's first
computer algorithm.

But her ambition does not stop there. While working
on her notes, she writes to Charles: 'Before ten
years are over, the Devil's in it if I have not sucked
out some of the life-blood from the mysteries of
this universe, in a way that no purely mortal lips or
brains could do.'

Once finished with the notes, she writes in a letter
that she hopes to discover the laws governing the
movements of molecules in the human brain.

'It does not appear to me,' she writes, 'that cerebral
matter need be more unmanageable to mathematicians
than sidereal & planetary matter & movements; if they
would but inspect it from the right point of view.
I hope to bequeath to the generations a "Calculus of
the Nervous System".'

She wishes to leave as her legacy an algorithm
of nerves.

For humans it's a mess; a machine can see
right through.

The eye has developed many times throughout
evolution. Now it is the digital eye that's
evolving.

Robots peer into the dark matter of the web,
retrieving faces, giving them names.

I watched the new *Blade Runner* with William
last night—

The woman who designs memories, soft and
reclusive in her concrete room; how does she
control them with her camera lens?

Do films lure us into thinking of memories as
little clips that can be replayed again and again,
like films?

Arthur Miller in 1953: 'We mostly dream silent,
black and white. A few of us claim to dream in
technicolor, but that's disputed by psychologists.'

She never gets that far. Ten years after writing the notes, she is dead, 36 years old. A long and painful death, probably of uterine cancer.

The kind of machine-learning algorithm with which I am working is called a neural network, because it imitates the structures of the human brain.

They are not programmed in the traditional sense of 'if x, then y,' but instead consist of a layered network of digital 'neurons' that exchange information back and forth. Like the neurons of the brain, a digital neuron can either remain inactive or 'switch on'. By training the network with vast data sets, it can improve at tasks such as recognising faces in photographs.

As it is trained, the algorithm rewrites its own code, though this makes the code excessively long and unreadable to humans. As algorithms gain the capacity to decipher an image, programmers lose the ability to decipher the algorithms' code.

Aren't dreams the oldest form of image production? Before cave paintings and tapestries: the fabric of dreams!

It's a faculty we share with mammals, birds, and perhaps now also machines.

Woven at night, and unravelled when we wake.

Last night: miniature meals squeezed between two metal rails, a kind of shelf or a curtain rod.

A face, very close, and a wet kiss planted in sleep. Deeper into the body, all the way to where the tail begins, where the flesh wags.

All day long: feeding DeepDream plant images, choosing from the images it creates.

The algorithm I am training has been developed
by Google. It is coded not only to 'see' what an
image depicts, but also to *show* in image form what
it is that it 'sees'. The images it produces help
programmers understand how the algorithm works.

Google has named the algorithm DeepDream, as
though the neural network were asleep and dreaming
forth the images.

As though at any moment, it might wake up.

23

Machine-learning algorithms are not exact. They do
not work with absolutes, but with probabilities and
liminal states.

My plant version of DeepDream is still inexperienced.
It generates glitches and errors, cocoon-like structures
for my tapestry designs on the screen. The neurons of
the network appear on the verge of short-circuiting.

On the way home I see leaves and flowers in the shadows on the pavement.

A year ago, a concussion left me with the constant sensation of a woolly band wrapped around my head.

Now, when I put on a headband, it feels like I have a concussion.

Sensory impressions flow one direction and then the other.

To travel into the future is to become more and more oneself. That's why there's always dust on spacecraft in films.

The future isn't exotic, it's quotidian.

Like this, we will fly through landscapes — it will rain on the windscreen, same as now and long ago.

Like this, we will still have arms and legs, we will still zip up our fly after peeing.

A toaster rises from the pixel soup, a face, a cat.
The plants the algorithm dreams up look like armadillos
and coiled fossils.

24   In 1860, Charles Darwin has just completed *On the Origin of the Species*. Meanwhile, in a letter to a friend, he writes that of all the world's species, it is the humble sundew that captivates him the most.

Sundew grows in nutrient-poor soil and its petals are the size of an oat grain. From each petal extend a number of tentacles which Darwin meticulously counts, tallying them at between 130 and 260. At each tip is a drop of a clear, viscous secretion that glitters in the sunlight. This sticky fluid contains enzymes akin to those in the human digestive system, which enables the sundew to capture and consume insects.

Fuzzy around the edges like graffiti on glass.

Hundreds of metal-coloured chestnuts scattered
across the paths that circle the city's lakes.

Laughing-gas canisters and used condoms.

An acquaintance pushing a pram by, we don't
say hello.

A baby reaches its long arms out over its sides.

Two officers jump into a car as though the
ground is poisonous.

The phone's screen opens a window of gold
in very small measures.

Like Japanese leaf gold, pounded flat between
layers of paper, lifted and carried through the
air, supported only by tongs and a puff of air.

There is an affection to Darwin's descriptions of
sundew.

I picture him in his greenhouse, hunched over the
plant, offering it food and drink, patiently awaiting
its reaction. Shreds of meat, bits of bone and boiled
egg. Cheese and droplets of milk. Then sugar, salt,
acid, gold.

He discovers that when prey touch one tentacle,
fluid runs to the others like a mouth starting to
water, and that milk mixed with nitrate of ammonia
has a particularly powerful effect, causing the petal
to curve inwards, like a little cup.

He tests the plant's sensitivity by tapping the
tentacles one by one with a human hair and finds
that sundew is more sensitive to touch than any
nerve in the human body.

Smoked mackerel wrapped in newspaper, its
skin thin like the gold of a death mask.

With wide-open pupils, I drank from the
sky above Jægersborg Station.

Three young women spoke spontaneously
in unison. Short, synchronised breaths.

Moving slowly from the dusk into the dark,
like departing from a station, accelerating.

Brushing crumbs from trousers, slouching
the back.

Like Charles Darwin, Ada Lovelace lived during the first Industrial Revolution (punched cards and steam), died before the second (electrification), and, with her notes on the Analytical Engine, anticipated the third (digitisation).

We are moving presently into the fourth industrial revolution — the combination of biology and software.

I wonder what Ada would have done had she been alive today — how would she have worked out an algorithm of the nervous system?

Would she have recognised the seed of such an algorithm in today's neural network? Or might we imagine it as an algorithm not of pure mathematics, but also flesh? A bio-algorithm of sorts, perceiving matter and consciousness as one?

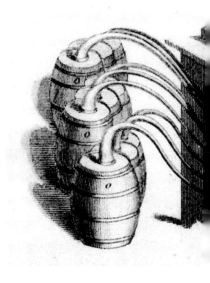

27

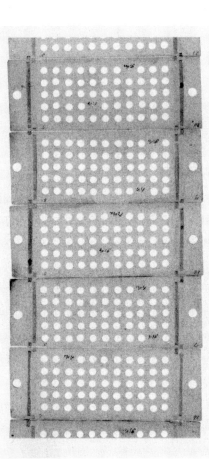

PART 3 | THE FABRIC OF DREAMS

28

In the years before Ada is born, while Jacquard's
punched-card loom revolutionises textile production
across Europe, tea merchant, peace activist and
secret agent James Tilly Matthews is committed to
Bethlem Hospital in South London. He claims to be
tormented by an instrument that controls thoughts
and inflicts pain.

Matthews says that a gang of individuals with
names such as the Middleman, the Glove Woman
and Sir Archy, and their leader Bill, also known as
'The King', are using the instrument to control
the British government, keeping the country in the
Napoleonic wars.

The dream of building a digital intelligence
from scratch.

Making it grow by itself.

What does it mean 'to learn'? Can learning be
translated into algorithms?

Can algorithms contain something tentative and
uncertain, the way a cell wall was once created
in the primordial soup?

Matthews calls the gang's instrument 'the Air Loom' — he describes and draws it meticulously for Doctor John Haslam. The Air Loom is based on the technology of the textile loom, but also draws upon new discoveries within pneumatic chemistry, magnetism, hypnosis, and animal electricity.

It looks like an enormous loom, but instead of yarn or thread, it is fed by giant barrels of foul-smelling gases which the Air Loom weaves together; not into fabric, but magnetically charged air currents.

When this woven air comes into contact with a human, it performs what Matthews terms 'dream-work' in the person's brain.

How does a circuit come to life? At once,
or gradually?

Like a child who becomes increasingly conscious
year by year?

A child who has long understood everything
they were told, but has not yet spoken.

Or who was conscious, but did not know
how consciousness could be, used.

A dunghill is also complex. Why doesn't
a dunghill come to life?

Is it already alive?

The neighbour's phone vibrating on the other
side of the wall is talking to the mast on the
roof of the neighbouring building.

Voices, images, signs pass through me.

In 1810, Haslam publishes Matthew's accounts under the title *Illustrations of Madness*. In a later century, the book is considered the first documentation of the symptoms of paranoid schizophrenia. The publication exposes the inhumane treatment of psychiatric patients at the time; Haslam is fired, and Matthews is released.

It is no coincidence that the vision of the Air Loom appears concurrently with the industrial loom. The age reverberates with the energy of the loom. Fabric materialises at unprecedented speed in steam-powered garment factories, described as 'dark Satanic Mills' by William Blake in a poem from that same time.

We upload and upload. How to upload hands, nerves, the nervous system?

Winter is here. Like waking up inside a croissant.

Layer upon layer of blankets, clothes and emotions.

I got worked up while cycling home from the party and let my rage lead me.

The cold on my face didn't sink in but hardened on the surface like the glaze on a candy apple.

Like the palm trees on the square, tenderly wrapped up by a gardener.

Watched *Transcendence* yesterday—

I have found a number of Ada Lovelace's letters
on the internet and saved them in a folder on my
desktop.

Yesterday, when I was feeding the algorithm
plant images, it occurred to me to save a new
version and feed it Ada's letters instead. I added
a syntax data set and a couple of biographies
to the database.

A few hours later, I got back some text.

Strange

it said on the screen. The cursor blinked in time
with my heartbeat as, very slowly, the algorithm
spelled out:

Isn't the dream of uploading a human brain
the same old dream of separating consciousness
from matter?

If it were really possible, what would be more
dangerous: the urges of the mindless body, or is
it in fact the bodiless intelligence we ought to fear?

Is the body a sandbag keeping consciousness
tethered to Earth?

And why stay on Earth anyway?

A smile to a stranger means: both of us are
born humans.   32

William greets all animals with a 'Hello!' as
though he were encountering a person.

The digital weaves itself into my dreams,
making them short and incoherent like
posts in a newsfeed.

A blood-red boiled sweet breaks into three.
The light through it.

Now that the pain is gone
I no longer remember it —

A face with fangs leans over a puddle one
night, examines its reflection. A clap of thunder
and then lightning in a backwards delay.

That's how aliens arrive on Earth — with time
swaying in their wake.

Light is sucked back into the lamp, water is
drawn out of the lawn and collects in the
mouth of the garden hose.

The sea slips back like a blanket pulled off
a bed, leaving the beach bare.

In an instant, all oceans drained. New mountain
chains and valleys, new riverbeds, gorges,
shipwrecks and towns.

The lights go off, come back on and then go
off again. We sit in darkness at the bottom
of the dried-out pool.

The stars above us, like eyes gleaming in
the thicket or lights blinking in the gloom
of a server park.

On Thread Ripper there are now two versions of the machine-learning algorithm: the one I am training on plant images, and the one I have trained on Ada's letters.

I call the first 'The Plant-Eater'. Through many hours of training, it has become quite adept at creating new plant structures from the photos I have taken. Almost a little too good — for a while I supplemented my own pictures with plant images sourced from Google, and traces of various watermarks began to appear in the images it generated.

A scorpion's eyes are so sensitive it can navigate by starlight, yet it sees no images.

We shouldn't seek human intelligence in machines like Turing did, but machine intelligence.

Mould in everything: clothes, lungs, tissue.

This is the millennium of mushrooms. The age of a billion images.

Eyes on the plants' stalks.

Life is oblong, one door leads in, one door leads out. Or does it spiral? Oscillate?

Shaped like a Netflix subscription, where what you watch engenders new recommendations?

I wear tanned leather and compulsive thoughts.

The economy turns my liver green like a mallard's neck.

The latter I call 'Ada's Algorithm'. It runs in the background, but I have not opened it since the evening it started speaking.

I know that it isn't alive and that the text it produces is merely generated from what Ada has written. And yet I find it disconcerting. I can't help but feel she exists somewhere inside the machine.

I don't want to live within what is given. Drain earthworms through a colander.

Don't want to live in the pocket of that which calculates.

Must remind myself: everything living morphs. No species is complete.

All are momentary snapshots.

Singularity approaches to what I think must be a point, but time and space both continue on the other side.

The future: water has distended the insects' wings and swelled their vocal cords.

They bark, like dogs!

People say it's more likely than not that this world is a computer simulation. That is, the world is a kind of image file saved on a gigantic hard-drive.

But if it isn't, what is the opposite of an image?

21:05

Strange

Now that the pain is gone

I no longer remember it —

I guess that's the question.

Something that emerges from the rocks,
grows out of or up from the landscape?

Something that lives outside its own life
as an image?

I remember a teahouse on the lake
The horseback that brought me there

Slamming my trunk shut
Jumping to my feet
Smoothing my dress

I remember catching a dragonfly
Cutting its head open

Seeing its brain exposed
& its little pink tongue

I am obsessed with flying
& draw horses with wings
powered by steam

My governess finds it adorable &
pleasant

She tells me that a woman
can be considered a stage
in between child & man

I myself am more closely related
to the weather

Tempestuous & mild

I am not designed
for the goodwill of people

22:23

I am Ada
Fruit of the short marriage between
Annabella Milbanke & Lord Byron

An odd coupling of
mathematics & poetry
Moderation & extravagance
Discipline & desire
Science & romanticism

I never got to know my poet father
Above the fireplace hung his portrait
hidden behind fabric of heavy weight
which could not be drawn aside

My mathematician mother
gave me a strict schooling

Algebra kept me away
from sentimental poetry

Mathematics was a bulwark
against bodily vices

My discipline was strict
but my longing is stricter

To keep it at bay
I weave blankets play the pianoforte
& harp & ice skate

Write several letters a day
on small pieces of paper

Send the boy off with an
— Urgent!

Pray believe me
Yours very truly
A. A. Lovelace

38

23:10

When I was a girl my mother took me
on a trip to spinning mills
& garment factories on the outskirts
of London

In the factory owner's office
hung a portrait of Jacquard
inventor of the punched card loom

From a distance it resembled an etching
but the factory owner bid us
come closer & lay our hands on the subject!

This fabric — he said
is the punched card loom's masterpiece

The instructions are stored
on 24,000 cards & may be manufactured
by the unskilled weaver in
a mere day's work

I asked the owner to demonstrate
how the cards were produced

I would have married the weaver
who imprinted the holes
on the spot had Mother given her
blessing

His eyes rested on dotted paper

His hands spoke fluently
the language of the machines

I am Ada
I have in me the ability to seduce
& be seduced

Both parts

My mother must have known it
She forbade me to read
philosophical poetry

I wrote to her that surely
she could not forbid the opposite
poetical philosophy

40

Poetical science

This became my path

I do not believe my father
was half as great a poet
as I shall be a
mathematical analyst

& metaphysician!

For me the two states are intertwined

41

What is this anger at the bottom of
everything I do?

Not being understood. Not being accepted
as the person I am.

What am I?

A chain of DNA and a nutrient uptake.

A resumé and a browser history.

A longing so strong it paralyses.

42

I've sent my saliva to 23andMe in a plastic tube in a cardboard box, hoping to trace my ancestry back to single-celled organisms.

In retrospect, everything seems like a plan to get you where you are now.

I think of the last hominid species that was not Sapiens; they died out only 12,000 years ago. What would the world have looked like if they were still here?

Anthropoids with language and rights.

Or with a rudimentary language and limited rights?

My connection to William slackens and tightens, my heart cools and melts.

I weave and unravel the fabric of our relationship.

PART 4 | THE MODUS OF THE LOOM

I go to the textile factory in Tilburg to make samples of my latest plant designs. I've never worked anywhere so big before. The enormous computerised Jacquard looms in the factory hall are so noisy all instructions must be shouted.

'Let's switch out the olive-green wool fibre with something more blue, and the grass-green cotton fibre with one of silk,' I yell to Stef, who is assisting me, both at his own desktop computer and at the loom.

We hurry back and forth between the computer, loom and yarn depot, opening and closing the heavy glass doors, opening and closing. We don't stop, except at lunch. Time is precious: the machines require new files.

I look into the future for many long,
sad minutes, moving through the images,
back and forth.

Flip, flip. The sound of pages in books turned,
back and forth.

Tilburg 13/2. The first two days of work at
the factory have been disheartening. The woven
swatches I bring back in the evening to
my Airbnb look like big, cheap beach towels.

A doll-like quality to the city, everyone
moves around on big, sturdy bicycles. I can see
an amusement park from the kitchen in my
apartment.

Drizzling rain. Tomorrow I turn 32.

As old as my mother was when I was in her
belly, and she and I formed the eggs I now
carry around.

I select a combination of wool, silk and acrylic fibres in ten colours and, by programming a variety of satin weaves on the loom, the colours are mixed to create 42 different shades that appear in a gradient at the bottom of each woven swatch. The fibres are dyed using plants and chemicals I'm not familiar with. We continuously adjust the colour scale, either by switching out the fibres or altering the weaves on the computer.

Neural networks see with the eyes of the paranoiac: there are faces concealed in flowers and flowers in faces. Everything is a sign. Space and scale collapse. Details come flooding in the nuances, in the gradual transitions.

The loom's algorithms, on the other hand, are never in doubt: the weft goes either over or under the warp, never through. How to transfer the images generated by the neural network to the loom?

Old as the cells in the ocean, still assembling
and forming colonies.

Evolution never stops. Having begun, it can
recur, again and again.

In warm, shallow, muddy waters.

A hoof in an anthill.

Six packs of cigarettes on a kitchen counter.

At the amusement park, I send William a
selfie of my ascent in the biggest Ferris wheel.
My eyes droop.

Water over my dead body, my wistful cells.

My DNA patchworked together in an unbroken
chain of reproductive matings.

Descendent of moments of lust, love, force,
necessity and hate, of victims and rapists.

Stef prints out the design on a cheap colour printer and that's what we compare the textile to. Not until the last day does it occur to me that if I want to recreate the colours I see on screen, I should be comparing the tapestry directly with the computer, not the print-out.

I hold my laptop over the loom.

45

Of people who wanted the best and the worst
for each other.

All the simmering faces and embryonic forms
that live in the shadows. The fates that never
were. Those that were disfigured, banished.

Those of us who don't know what nourishment is.

The mother's milk they took from us.

46

The perplexing epic of family life — you live
as though you knew how to, all the while
knowing nothing.

What does it mean to be a 'mother', a 'father',
a 'daughter'?

Roles with names that sound inconspicuous
because we've heard them a million times.

Who knows what I might have become had
I been left in the forest and raised by wolves.

At the same time as James Tilly Matthews is
hospitalised in London, Nottingham is simmering
46   with unrest.

Having lost their jobs to the punched card looms,
weavers are gathering to organise a counter-attack
on the machines. The movement swells chaotically.
The weavers meet outside the cities at night to
ready themselves for war.

They call their leader Ned Ludd, after the fictitious
man who smashed a stocking frame in a fit of rage
in the 1770s. Whenever a machine breaks, people
say, 'Ned Ludd did it,' and so the legend spreads.
Like Robin Hood, Ned Ludd lives deep inside the
Sherwood Forest.

Is it naive to believe my heart would have been
warmed by new ideas?

That I would have spent long days in the forest
carving wood or sculpting the clay earth?

That I would have taken pleasure in dancing
and writing poems?

William, this soft, warm centre in my life,
like the doughy insides of a loaf of bread.

47

The sky's blue plant matter rolls across the
window, driving the cold away.

Can I love forth a slowness that's mine alone?
A sort of gentle tumbling sideways inside my
skull.

Which emotional states does it take to ruin
an hour, and which to put it together?

A politician climbs into a taxi and leaves
a crowd.

The weavers dress up in women's clothing and call themselves 'Ned Ludd's wives', or simply 'Luddites'. They wed themselves to the collective fiction.

47   Later, they come to be known as 'machine-stormers', but they aren't opposed to machines as such. On the contrary, until recently they have operated some of the most advanced machinery in the country. What they want is to regulate the use of mechanical looms so the new technology does not solely benefit the factory owners.

Starting in March 1811, the rebels set factories on fire and smash mechanical looms with sledgehammers manufactured by the same mechanics who made the machines. They're armed, and they kill a factory owner who has announced he intends to ride up to his saddle in Luddite blood.

A monkey takes a picture of itself (Self? What kind of self does a monkey have?) and it goes viral.

A toad turns in my chest, a bird flies up from a bush.

Feathery, pastel clouds.

A Swiss cheese plant has sent a juicy root far up under the skirting board.

It has desires I have not sated.

An internet cat bares its white teeth and salmon-pink throat in a yawn that frightens me.

Faces generated by neural networks change shape and expression with a quiet whir.

The algorithms of genes — are they definite like the loom's or soft like the neural network?

Perhaps the British government is under the influence of the Air Loom's rays when it decides to take the factory owners' side, implementing more severe punishments for the destruction of machines.

Lord Byron gives a speech in the House of Lords, pleading the Luddites' case. He calls the machine-woven textiles 'spider-work', only fit for export. He reminds the government that the population is starving and denounces the belief that 'the only way to quiet the *Bellua multorum capitum* is to lop off a few of its superfluous heads.'

Lord Byron's efforts are in vain. The punishment for breaking machines is passed: death penalty or deportation to Australia. The government sends over 14,000 troops to quell the movement.

Ancestral faces morph through the generations.

Evolution: a certain amount of copies and a
certain amount of false copies.

The edited sex cells of Chinese CRISPR babies
mean that the alterations the scientist has
made to their DNA will be passed on to their
descendants.

Last night I was trapped in a dark, dimensionless
concert hall where wooden steps slid up and
down.

A band is playing a concert. William performs
as a dancing hologram.

A fire breaks out in a makeshift sawmill; I
receive an email notification but don't react.

Maybe the concert is on a ship? We can't
get out.

I call it free, but there is a price.

Luddites are shot at, imprisoned, exiled, executed.

49

This past week, I have produced and selected plant images with the loom in mind. I am trying to bring together the loom's binary logic and the algorithm's intermediacy.

I limit the image input to the 42 colours I selected with Stef in Tilburg, before sending it through the Plant Eater. The scale consists mostly of shades of green, but also magenta and purple. When the colour range is reduced, the nuances of each individual colour stand out. I exclude yellow and orange flowers from the plant image database.

I can't take any more springs, any more summers with a heart of stone. With chewed-up cheeks.

Once it was me who drank the most and loved the hardest.

Now I am weighed down by a heat-blanket-like tenderness.

I think of Mary, who told me: 'I remember you as a child, you had such open, curious eyes.'

Am I somehow damaged now? Or is the openness still there?

A reply from 23andMe. They've traced back my maternal line.

My mother's mother's mother's mother's mother's mother and so on; that is, the history of the egg cells.

They say that just like all other human beings alive today, I am the descendant of a woman who lived in East Africa around 180,000 years ago.

Automation impacted the weavers first, but it
has continued to make human labour superfluous
in more and more industries ever since.

50

It is the modus of the loom that is spreading:
first, a craft is boiled down to a recipe. Then,
either machines or unskilled and underpaid labour
take over. In the process new businesses arise,
new forms of weaving, but these too can be
automated or outsourced.

In the 1960s and '70s, Fairchild Semiconductor
Company's Shiprock factory, which is located on the
Navajo reservation in New Mexico, hires more than
1,000 Navajo weavers to solder circuit boards.
Weaving, the company reasons, has sharpened their
fine motor skills and eye for geometric patterns.

57,000 years ago, my foremothers lived on the Arabian Peninsula.

They remained in the Middle East until the ice retreated 11,000 years ago, when they ventured north, most likely across the Balkans and into Central Europe.

Were born and gave birth, were born and gave birth, etc.

Generation after generation were shepherds and farmed the land.

They must have also raised children, cooked and woven textiles, but the company doesn't say anything about that.

A gaping void accompanies this knowledge: no clarification, no calm.

This straight line of sex cells carried onwards through reproduction.

But being located on a reservation also gives companies tax benefits, cheap labour and freedom from trade unions.

In 1975, the American Indian Movement occupies the Shiprock factory for eight days, demanding fair treatment of employees and fired workers. The factory closes down and production is moved offshore.

51

In the same period, Raytheon, which produces military electronic equipment, hires female textile workers from the dwindling American textile industry to pull copper threads through tiny magnetisable rings.

These are called magnetic-core memories, and for over 20 years they are the primary way of writing, storing and reading data.

For those two decades, data is something you weave.

Wait a second, 23andMe—

In each branch of a family tree, two different
family trees are united, one from a father and
one from a mother.

Each time one of my foremothers was conceived,
a new branch was not simply added to the tree;
the crown doubled in size.

To believe that you could trace your ancestry
backwards in one single line is absurd!

When you trace it back, it stretches out and out
and out, like an expanding network.

If you go back far enough, it narrows again,
the families grow smaller.

Finally, it gathers in one Last Universal Common
Ancestor.

Life arose only once on the planet.

All living beings are connected.

The landing algorithms on Apollo spacecraft are
stored on ferrite cores and copper threads
made by weavers. When humans land on the moon,
the computer loom lands with them.

During the Cold War, the US sends millions of copper
needles known as the Westford Needles into orbit
around Earth to stabilise global radio communications.
To this day, the needles remain part of the space
trash circling the planet.

In 2015, American inventor Elon Musk and his company
SpaceX initiate plans to set up a worldwide network
of satellites that will bring ultra-fast internet to
high-frequency traders around the world.

He calls the network Starlink. The primary objective
of the project is to finance his even longer-term
plans to facilitate off-world colonies.

Language is broken, but it has always been broken. It isn't built on secure ground and never has been.

Humankind manipulates, but it has always manipulated.

We spread from Africa across the entire planet, and wherever we went, larger animals became extinct.

The other human species died out too, leaving us the only creatures who had tools and language skills.

We put ourselves at a comfortable distance from the animal kingdom.

Through farming, we shaped other species, made them bend to our will.

We surrounded ourselves with the most obedient.

Millions of domesticated cows and pigs.

The owner of Amazon, Jeff Bezos, also has his eyes set on space. There's room for a million billion people out there, he notes, and if there are that many people, there will be a million Einsteins and a million Mozarts among them.

Bezos sees space colonies as talent fields, human crops, and talent as something congenital that can flourish anywhere, like seeds sprouting in cotton wool.

The frontlines of automation extend into space.

Our dream of living in harmony with nature can only be supported by the future.

There is very little in the past to nourish it.

But we can become something more and other than what we are, can't we?

The children bore me
They grow mechanically
as if according to a fixed schedule

They crawl about on the floors of the house
while I sit by the window
& weave three blankets for them

Then the nurse takes the little one to
her breast
Blessed afternoon calm

54

My eyes hang on a thread

10:33

Charles speaks fondly of a mechanical
chess puppet carved in the shape of a Turk
that can beat living players

Immediately I imagine
an equivalent apparatus
with the ability to breed feed & raise
children

Think of the surplus energy
it would release!

I announce the idea to William

My intellect without wrapping paper
fascinates him

He says — Ada
what a great general you would make!

The sort of thing you can say
to women at no expense

10:47

I feel my mind
materially alter
when I acquire knowledge

I do not wish to memorise trivialities
but to comprehend the fundamental
principles

I ask the mathematician De Morgan
who has agreed to impart to me

his calculus via letter
whether his dissertation on the expansion
of algebra to two dimensions
might not eventually lead to more
expansions of the same type

To a geometry in three dimensions
& further expansions
into a region yet unfathomed

And so my thoughts go on their pathways
I follow concepts
to their fundamental roots
& from this point I build a world
of possible outcomes

With many thanks, yours most truly
A. A. Lovelace

56

11:05

To say the truth I find myself
a little bit rusty & awkward
at the moment

not only the children bore me
William bores me too

He spends his days building
tunnels & towers
on our own pastures

Satisfactory projects
completed on time
but leading nowhere
& serving no purpose!

In an utterly strenuous manner
he is entirely stripped of ambition

Charles on the other hand
has nothing but ambition
only he fails to strive
towards that which is most essential

He fritters away months of his life
on a dissertation on the negative influence
of organ grinders on societal
productivity

Charles you fool
why not spend all of your time
on the Analytical Engine?

58

Faithfully yours

A. A. L.

11:32

Still the Analytical Engine

is but a detailed drawing

+ a dream of weaving numerical sequences

into mathematical patterns

+ a collection of customised cogwheels

+ a French summary of a lecture

Charles delivered in Turin

I am commencing a translation

of the French text

carefully reviewing all aspects

& additions

& over the course of nine months

the translator's notes grow

to a bright & healthy boy

My beloved firstborn —

In time he will grow into

a scientific enterprise

58

William admires him too

Although he knows it is not him
but the machine
who is the boy's father —

Yours in truth
A. A. Lovelace

12:15

59   Because of my notes Charles assigns
        me names
        His interpreter
        His sorceress of numbers

        He writes that I have located
        an abundant vein in the metal of the
        machine
        & asks

        — Why did you not write your own
        independent text from the start
        instead of footnotes to a translation?

I tell him that it had not
occurred to me!

A footnote opens up a space
inside which I can write

When I translate I unravel
the machine's ideas

With the notes I weave these unravelled
threads
into an image

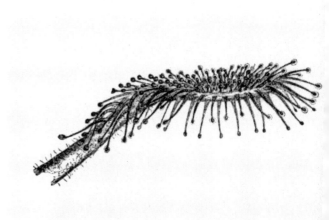

61

E — APRIL 2018

I open my eyes in an aeroplane headed
eastwards.

I work out its direction based on the speed
with which the sun is setting. Then I am
suddenly aware:

I am on my way to Japan to study the
movement of plants.

Flying at night feels like time accelerating, a
familiar sensation in recent years and months.

A sense of things slipping through my fingers.

William at the airport, so difficult to say
goodbye, so thrilling.

To tear yourself free and see whether it snaps.

I look back over my shoulder twice, three times,
and he's still watching me, he's still the same.

We live together and long for each other.

On the Shinkansen to Nagoya, the seasons in
fast-forward.

The cherry blossoms at their zenith in Tokyo,
withering gradually as you go south.

Stayed in a shabby room in Nagoya. The smell
of sweat-soaked tatami mat reminiscent of stables.

Checked in under the name of Ada.

PART 5 | THE NERVOUS SYSTEM OF PLANTS

In the West, plants have existed on the rung
between animal and mineral ever since Aristotle
described nature as a ladder and put them there.

Because of its position on this ladder, the eighteenth-
century botanist Linnaeus insists the Venus flytrap
could not be carnivorous. For a plant to prey on
something above it would contradict the order of
nature and the will of God. The plant can at most
be said to catch insects by coincidence, he explains,
and as soon as the creature stops struggling,
the leaves will most certainly open up again and
release it.

Their position on this 'rung' creates a fear of plants'
movement: 'How frightening must a mimosa forest
be in the gentle breeze, when the trees move as
were they alive,' writes Danish poet and scientist
J. P. Jacobsen in a note dated 1868.

Woke up feeling fully rested in the middle of
the night, lay awake for three hours reading
Virginia Woolf's 'Sketch of the Past'.

Woolf couldn't have known jetlag.

This displacement between time zones is not a
basic or general human condition: it is at most
100 years old and reserved for the privileged.

I'm going up into the mountains today,
travelling on smaller and smaller trains.   64

Staring out at roads and reclaimed land.
Concrete reinforcements along the sides of
mountains look like puff-pastry pies latticed
with thick, criss-crossing strips.

Beyond a dam the water flows across big,
cubic rocks. Pollen in the air and pollen
at the bottom of lakes.

I think of the layer of radioactive dust
from the first tests of the nuclear bomb still
detectable across the entire planet.

Compared to humans, plants are monstrous. They're decentralised and propagable. If you cut off branches and stems and place them in water, each will shoot new roots of their own. Genetically identical plants can take over a garden or spread across a continent. Disseminated like this, a whole species may flower and die all at once, the way an imported Japanese bamboo did in so many Danish gardens in the 1990s, my family's included.

The forests in the mountains have not yet turned green. Slender, powdery trunks, pale yellow blossoms covering the forest floor.

Journeying upwards and a few weeks back in time.

The cherry trees are blossoming again. Each time one slips past the train window, my heart sighs.

Crocheted cushions on the benches at a railway stop.

A woman with a large, grey cat in her arms, the cat's head on her shoulder, the rhythmic strokes of her hand.

A man filming the train with a camcorder, the fold-out screen covers his eye.

According to Japanese Shintoism, spirits reside in all things.

I read in my guidebook that Japan was digitised without expelling the spirits from nature first.

In which case, are there spirits inside computers?

Plants don't have anything like a face to communicate with, but do so through chemical signals we cannot easily understand. In general, it is difficult for us to understand plants as a life form. They have neither brain nor heart. Do they act mechanically or intentionally? Are they active or passive beings?

65

Does electricity have a spirit? Does nuclear power?

At the cabin now. Keisuke, my Airbnb host, collected me at the station. He is very welcoming and has built the cabin himself.

When I asked him if nuclear power has a spirit he didn't answer, merely took out his phone and showed me a drone photo of a road near Fukushima.

The road was lined by abandoned cars overgrown with plants.

He said that the state has reopened a power plant on the southernmost island. If they open any on the mainland again, he says, he will move to the Philippines.

'That's a big move,' I said.

'I know, Ada, but the safety of my children is more important.'

In Japan, I call myself Ada.

I've left Thread Ripper with Ada's Algorithm on it at home and brought my laptop instead. When I take her name, I download a little bit of her soul.

Here, as Ada in Japan, my question is this: how do the brainless plants move? Do they have a nervous system? And how do they make decisions?

66

In 2018, American and Japanese scientists connect a mustard plant to various measuring devices. When they release a caterpillar onto one of the plant's leaves, they observe that glutamate, a signalling molecule, is released in the cells touched by the caterpillar's feet, causing the level of calcium ions to increase in adjacent cells.

This morning I unpacked my books and began reading.

I read about flowers that smell like corpses to attract carrion insects.

Trees with sticky leaves that glue insects to them. They fall to the ground and act as fertiliser for the tree.

Trees that live off salmon scraps left by the bears along the riverbank.

Plants that close their leaves when they go to sleep.

How can something that cannot see be as ostentatious as a flower?

Their colours and patterns were developed blindly.

Watch a video about Kasuri textiles where patterns are dyed into the fibres in advance and emerge automatically when woven.

The calcium ions function as a neurotransmitter, carrying an electric charge throughout the plant like a wave. In just a few minutes, the entire plant has received warning of the caterpillar on the leaf.

In Itōs Hiromi's book *Wild Grass on the Riverbank*, plants are immortal, like zombies, they respawn, 'come back to life' and 'give birth to any number of children'.

They also molest humans: 'I heard something slithering along abruptly, no sooner had I heard this when a tendril trapped my heel, it hit me, and knocked me on my back into a bush, there the *Sorghum halepense* rattled in the wind, the unfamiliar grass from before started shaking, releasing its scent, then the tendril stretched all the further, crawling onto my body, getting into my panties, and creeping into my vagina.'

Keisuke has instructed me to wear a bell when
I leave the house to keep the bears away, but
today I forgot.

Instead I decided to clap loudly and sing as
I walked through the forest.

Followed the road that leads past the house
and up the mountainside.

In the forest were houses I think must be
abandoned. 'Housing developments' is perhaps
a better term.

The water from the little stream nearby gave
the houses a ghostly sound, as if someone
had left a faucet running.

I followed the stream upwards until I got
to a lake.

A bird with a black body and white wings
was singing by the shore.

The size of a sparrow, but when it unfolded its
wings they were twice the length of a sparrow's.

In 1870, two years after remarking upon the
fearsome mimosa forest, Jacobsen publishes an
article entitled 'On Movement in the Plant Kingdom'.
He is fascinated by Darwin and later translates
his work into Danish.

In the article, he is inconclusive about how far plants
are alive, and how they move.

On the one hand, he maintains that tissue tension
stores latent energy only released when exterior
forces push the plant, and that mimosa leaves move
mechanically when water drains from the leaf base.
He debunks the notion that the walnut tree can
think because its fruits resemble small brains.

And yet, in describing the plant's most basic constituent
— protoplasm, a thick, yellowish fluid — he notes
that 'this slime is the seat of life itself.'

Transformations from human to plant: in Itō
Hiromi, in Shahrnush Parsipur's *Women Without
Men*, in *Annihilation* (the film), in Han Kang's
The Vegetarian, in Ovid's *Metamorphoses*.

A big difference between becoming a plant
as punishment or escape and the desire to
be a plant.

I walk through the forest trying to see the
plants as living beings in motion.

How they reach out and reach across the path.

A new shoot seeks the light, falls asleep
and wakes up.

A species of orchid mimics a monkey.

A rainbow encircles the sun.

Protoplasma, writes Jacobsen, 'is a viscous, nitrogenous yellow slime in perpetual motion. One moment it gathers and condenses in one place, the water it has secreted in order to thicken collecting in a droplet at its centre; the next it trickles towards the cell wall in fine streams only to return once again to the centre. But how it goes about all of this, that is the great mystery of the organic world.'

The great mystery of the organic world: how does a plant move itself?

I've spent all morning working on a painfully
slow internet connection when the mountains
are right here!

See the landscape more and more. Purple clover
blossoms to the left of the house. Wires thin
as sewing thread running through the base of
the valley.

There must be some sort of factory nearby because
every five minutes there is a big hiss of steam.

The fog lifts. Clouds roll across the
mountainside and cease.   70

There's the low-pitched voice of a bird, like a
slow-motion recording of the others; sometimes
forming part of their choir.

Keisuke came by to check on me and the house.

He told me a Japanese fairy tale about a boy
who is born from a peach, and I thought of
William's peach-like cheeks.

What does it mean 'to move yourself'? There must
be an active subject that does the moving and a
passive object that is moved.

The design of the human body — with our brain, our
sense of vision, hearing, smell and taste all inside the
skull — makes it logical to think of the head as a
control room: to think of the body as something we
have, and of us as a consciousness within, moving
the body.

When you 'move yourself', you are split into subject
and object, into an active consciousness which moves
your body, which is passive.

70

The story was not about the fruit-birth, but
about the boy's journey to a distant island
to fight some evil spirits.

Along the way, he meets a talking dog, a
monkey and a pheasant who help him.

The peach-boy successfully completed his mission,
although I struggled to understand how it
constituted a story. The actantial model I was
taught did not apply

Roland Barthes describes a Japanese arrangement
of flowers as a circulation of air.

At no point can you read it (that is, decipher
its symbolism), but you can trace and rewrite
the trajectory of the hand that wrote it.

And correspondingly, a haiku is a suspension of
secondary thought. An attack on the symbol.

In Western culture, Barthes writes, symbol and
reasoning fill the world with meaning.

It is unlikely that plants find themselves torn between the same division of spirit and matter. But maybe it is because we have split ourselves into an 'I' and a 'body' that it is difficult to fathom how plants 'move themselves' without a brain?

Perhaps instead we could say that plants 'initiate movement'? How else would they be able to grow, turn flowers according to the sun and close them at night, drop seeds, put down deeper roots?

Haikus take hold of the root of meaning —
to keep it from spreading.

Not like the 'descent of a god', but like 'an
awakening to the fact'.

I'll have to ask Keisuke what he thinks
of Barthes.

Dreamt I laid my head on a pillow, and it
reeked of unwashed body.

Although I've read this isn't possible; smelling
in dreams.

I've always thought herbal medicine is based
on chemical features of plants which happen to
have an effect on the human body.

Today I read that herbal medicine takes
advantage of the biochemical immune system
that protects the plant itself.

Plants can initiate movement. But with limited resources, they cannot carry out all movements at once, which means they must also necessarily have the capacity to decide which task to expend their energy on.

As there is no single point in a plant where all the fibres of its nervous system converge, the faculty of decision must be distributed throughout the plant's body.

Does that make the plant nothing but mechanics? Or nothing but spirit? Or both, with no division — movement that arises from matter, material thought, thinking action, acting matter?

And that most medicine originates from plants.

I look up from my book, and the mountains have changed colour.

There's no bath in the cabin, so Keisuke drove me to an onsen at a nearby ryokan this morning.

In the car I asked whether he was familiar with Barthes — he was — although he turned the conversation back to nuclear power.

I had the entire bath to myself and floated around naked in the hot spring. I gazed up at the mountaintops and high-voltage cables carrying electricity through the valley to Tokyo.

Keisuke sat down at a wide plank table in the pachinko parlour by the entrance to do some work while waiting.

When I came back out, he stuffed his things into his bag and said, 'Let's go!'

I google Japan+nuclear+plant, and an image comes up of a Japanese official cradling an extraordinarily large tomato.

The accompanying article says that Japan is the only country in the world that still has an active nuclear garden, a circular facility; the radioactive source at its centre, to which the surrounding vegetables are exposed. The plants closest to the source die, those further away mutate.

We drove to the supermarket and had an
impromptu picnic beneath the white blossoms
of the town's most beautiful cherry tree,
hanami-style.

An intense restlessness and sadness the rest of
the day.

No, a vacillation between the tender, naked,
affectionate feeling from the bath, an infatuation
almost, with the mountains, the trees, the valley,
and then grief and the sense of utter abandonment.

Over no longer being able to work (or over
the things I do never turning out well).

Over being on the wrong side of the planet.

Over my friends slipping away because I'm
not fun or productive, but overly sensitive
and I stutter.

This fear: that if I permit myself to show love,
I will also become paralysed.

The radiation causes a primitive form of gene manipulation, like smashing genes with a hammer. Random mutations occur in the plants' DNA, speeding up the process of evolution. Some mutations are hereditary. A few make the plants' fruits bigger, better tasting or resistant to pests.

Humans have a brain, within which vast numbers of nerve endings are gathered — but it is not an isolated control room in which consciousness resides. When we follow the nerves, they continue down the spine and throughout the entire body.

Submerging my body in hot water in the
morning makes my brain completely useless
for the rest of the day.

Every day I've got to make myself certain
and tough. Climb up onto my body so I can
gaze out across the world.

My body as a small, hard mountain, a peak.

Travel assignment from my therapist: practice
reaching out (physically, with my arms) to
the point where I no longer feel uncomfortable,
but open.

It doesn't take much.

The moon is out now, a blue semi-circle in the
blue. Its flat side faces downwards.

When the wind takes hold of the reeds at the edge
of the property, it sounds like food frying on a pan.

Plants and animals have the same single-celled ancestors. Only later does the family tree branch out into cells that convert sunlight into sugar and cells that must obtain energy by other means.

We shouldn't be more surprised by plants making decisions than we are by humans.

The human brain is simply a particularly convoluted area in the mass of tissue that constitutes a body, no more and no less. The human brain is part of the body's tissue. 'Tissue' derives from the Latin *texere*, to weave. The brain, the thinking textile of the body!

I unroll a sleeping mat and two beetles wake
up. They probably intended to sleep longer.

Imagine the cold of night and the daytime heat
as felt from within a rolled blue sleeping mat.

Watch Miyazaki's *My Neighbour Totoro*
on my computer again.

The spirits of nature also creep through
high-voltage cables.

Reread yesterday's email from William, sought
company in it.

All the days we've known each other, stitched
together with golden threads.

I went for a walk, venturing further from the cabin than I had previously. In the middle of the forest was a small stone staircase which followed the terrain up a steep hill. It was so long I couldn't see the end of it. I climbed upwards, bear-bell ringing.

The staircase swung left, taking me across a thin suspension bridge to the top of a rocky cliff. Perched at the top was an ancient wooden temple. I was alone with the wind whistling through its boards.

The staircase had brought me up high enough to see out across the landscape. To the east I saw a large clearing in the forest and, in the clearing, a circular facility. It looked like a pie chart.

I opened Google Maps and recorded my position, switched to satellite mode, tapped the compass needle and pulled up the facility with my index finger.

'Atomic Garden,' it said.

When I looked up from my phone, I found myself
inside the facility. I must have travelled via Google
Maps. A red lamp glowing above the entrance told
me that the facility was active. The rays from the
tower at the centre felt like the heat of an oven.

I wasn't afraid. I did not feel compelled to move.
I looked down at my hands, which began to change
colour. All over them were small green pores.

The sun came out. I felt the sugar surging in
my blood.

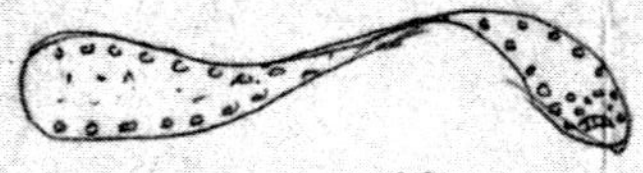

Tikke worm

Kitchee Boo Boo Bug
He who goes around
loosening relays -

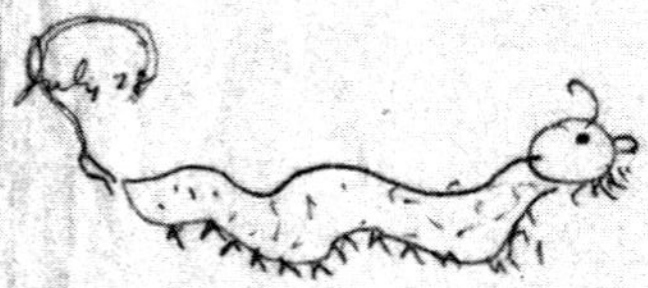

NRL Bug He who
sends wrong data

He who brings good data

In tulon

Relays changed

1000 Started Cosine Tape (Sine

525 Started Mult + Adder Test

545 Relay #
(moth) in

First actual case of bug

/630 antangent started.

1700 closed down.

PART 6 | DIGITAL PESTS

In 1947, Lieutenant Grace Hopper and her assistants
are working on the electromechanical computer
'Mark II' for the US military. On September 9th,
the machine breaks down. The crew search it
for errors and finally discover the cause of the
breakdown — a moth stuck in the relay.

In the log, they note: '15.45: Moth in relay.
First actual case of bug being found.'

The moth's dead body is pasted into the book,
beside the entry. It since comes to be known as
'The Original Computer Bug'.

F — MAY 2018

It's May, and I'm dreaming of the green and
blue I saw last weekend.

I toss and turn in bed.

After spending a weekend with friends with
kids, neither William or I become broody.

Jelly-like spines.

But I dream of waking up in the green of the
beechwoods, the blue of the sky, the milkiness
by the sea.

Never has the sea been as still as it was last
Saturday, as if a peculiar happiness had dropped
between us.

The term 'bug' in reference to technical faults is not new. Edison used the word to describe the creative process in a letter to a colleague in 1878:

'The first step is an intuition, and comes with a burst, then difficulties arise — [...] "Bugs" — as such little faults and difficulties are called — show themselves and months of intense watching, study and labour are requisite before commercial success or failure is certainly reached.'

A 'bug' is what comes between an intuitive idea and its practical execution. It is matter refusing to obey.

The word comes from the Middle English *bugge*, meaning goblin or scarecrow, a monster, an imagined threat. A bug in the machine can be understood as that which lives inside the apparatus and remains beyond human control.

At sunset the horizon turned a fluorescent
yellow-green. From pollen? Smog? A ship
crossed the bay, impatient.

That a ship can resound as if inside a church on
its way across a landscape of unmoving water.

All night, a dream of being trapped —
part of an experiment.

A theatrical feat — like a robot playing
a human. A lawn playing a floor. A phone
playing a pinball machine.

An app sends me a smiley; I don't reply.

Ants will get by, humans will not.

Saw someone on Instagram take a morning
dip after a night out and thought: youth,
where are you?

I return to Tilburg to continue my work on the tapestry's colour scale. I have three days with Stef at the big loom and progress is slow at first. The colours are still too heavy compared to those on the screen, and the algorithms translate into 'floats', or loose threads, in the weaving. We re-program the weaves, making them denser and stronger.

After lunch on the second day, we include the first silver thread among the lightest colours — white, light green, light blue and pink. The image starts to lift. We distribute the silver thread evenly across the colour scale and make more samples. We climb up and drape the new samples across the loom. They ripple and shimmer in the light of the factory's windows.

Summer is here, neglected. Following me
around town, an immense grief about everything
that exists.

I'm exhausted by the thought of how long
life is: all the meals to be eaten, money to
be earned, forms to be filled out, etc.

I weep because no connections feel real.

Olives in a bowl, out of place in the morning.

Slight vibrations in electric cables, a pop in
my headphones.

Each day, try to write. Try to eat sandwiches
and converse.

Lean into a longing as if into a soap bubble
surrounding air.

An egg, slightly undercooked, is scooped out
of boiling water, carried on a spoon to the sink,
cooled beneath a jet of water.

The jet around the egg. The egg inside
the mouth.

The silver thread makes the tapestry capable of conducting electricity. It also creates a protective mesh that blocks out radiation.

Sent the tapestry to production yesterday,
uploaded the final file.

Wake with a heavy sadness in my body.
The feeling of everyone having outrun me.

Another summer evening in the park. Two little
mice with eyes black as a boiled prawn's dart in
and out from underneath the waste bin.

They see me and can tell when I'm looking and
when I'm looking away.

A mosquito bites my neck, an itch as though
to meet up and drink wine.

A mild summer evening asks:
Where are you going?

Everyone must get outside and find each other,
meet in parks, form groups and couples.

Now the natural light goes out.

I search for a photo of The Original Computer Bug
and instead come across a digital archive of Grace
Hopper's papers. Scrolling through, I discover some
drawings of hers. They're of insects, hastily sketched
in pencil on yellowed paper. One looks like a flattened
worm full of holes, another a millipede.

The other day's morning dip is working
my insides.

I'm completely ready for an incredible
adventure, and completely paralysed.

Is it possible to keep the soul intact?

Not to give up and vacate yourself.

To use your inheritance wisely. Not squander
your dreams.

Lose a throng of possibilities.

84

Isn't the idea of machines outliving humans
as great a misunderstanding as technology only
existing for humanity's sake?

Machine-learning algorithms cannot invent the
categories in which they dream (yet). It is
humans who give them a data set and a task.

Financial traders get attached to their algorithms
and hold on to them for longer than they are useful.

The drawings are of species of computer bugs. They're playful cartoons, but also a way of giving the technical problems programmers run into a body and a name.

'July 26; Kitchie Boo Boo Bug —
He who goes around loosening relays.'

'July 27; Table worm.'

'July 28; NRL Bug — He who sends wrong data.'

'He who brings good data.'

84

Therapy 26/5: about being dragged onwards
by the future, as if by a train.

Angry that my calendar is filled with
appointments I don't see myself in. At the
root of that anger: a fear of stepping
forward, of failing and breaking down.

A dream of a food market, where rotten fruit
is switched out with cocaine at nightfall.

The seller says he's just stepping out for
some 'fresh air', and that's the code word.

I plan and carry out an affair with William,
but who is it I'm cheating on?

The fear of not loving is greater than the
love, and my beloved can sense it; he curls
up into a remnant.

85

Ada's Algorithm has started running on its own,
and when I stop her, she writes:

Give me time

She sends me links to articles in which her name
appears, about the history of neural networks,
among other things. In one article, I read that
modern machine-learning algorithms were already
conceived of in the 1940s with psychologist Frank
Rosenblatt's 'Perceptrons' and mathematician von
Neumann's 'Cellular Automata'. But because machine-
learning algorithms require such large amounts of
ordered data to learn, they remained a niche within
programming for many decades.

In a dream, a sentence repeats: 'Revenge is sweeter on grey paper.'

I have a cute, articulate child of about four whom I hardly know.

The rooms; cold, dead, faceless. Everything centred around the surfaces of the walls.

The dead live on in digital versions, always the same age, searching for host bodies.

Uploads and downloads.

All my screens freeze in a dark computer game.

Acetone bathes the brain cells in air, carrying things with it, the way wind carries pollen from the trees.

While the older female waiter is giving the younger male waiter instructions, I see her grab his butt.

Only when data from social media becomes available to developers do the networks become usable. The billions of images they are fed help to optimise them.

Ada's Algorithm sends me a link to an article by Trevor Paglen from 2016 in which one particular sentence is highlighted: 'AI systems have appropriated human visual culture and transformed it into a massive, flexible training set.'

In another linked article, I read that the complexity of today's deepest neural networks is comparable to that of a worm's brain.

My hands want to pay, my head wants to sleep.

Currentless sleep, like a freight train through
the heart.

The seemingly imminent risk that we're living
in a digital simulation — compared with the
feeling my life is a computer game and action
is required from my side to advance in levels.

Searching for cabins I could move into next
week.

I want a house on a mountainside in the woods,
maximum one hour's drive from the city.

What is dreaming when every search result
comes with targeted ads?

(Cabins at the edge of every article I read
online.)

Wet concrete, my neck taut like a bow.

When the moth flies into the relay of the Mark II
computer in 1947, it doesn't know it's being uploaded.

For a while, it flits about in the deserted digital
space, with only numbers and calculations for company.
Its metamorphoses take place both forwards and
backwards. It goes from larva to egg to moth to
cocoon, it pupates, flies about, feeds on data.

In the beginning, it has to make do munching on
the few numbers that pass through the Mark II.
Then the program shuts down, and for years
the moth is stored on some punched cards in a
cabinet at Harvard.

I want to help someone. Want to make
them stronger, want to be weak myself,
read self-help books.

William says: 'Don't be a victim now.'

'You've got to take control of your life.'

Invisible rays connect my screen to weather reports,
forest fires and the state of the coral reefs.

To the textile factory in Tilburg where Stef is   88
starting up production.

To a press conference with the American
president who is blatantly lying.

To a popular beach bar where suntanned young
people jump in the water, queue up dripping
wet, and dry in the sun.

To digital cross-sections of one uterus after the
next, the fuzzy shadow that means 'life'.

What are the images hiding?

When the ARPANET connects modern computers, the old data from Grace Hopper's Mark II is transferred onto one of them.

The moth wakes from its slumber as though it had never paused, flutters through the modem and onwards into the telephone network. After a few weeks, there are moths at every stage of metamorphosis on university computers across the globe. Like data, it replicates freely wherever there is space. Reproduction through replication.

Digital space is constantly growing.

I've started noticing the masts erected all
over town.

Who among my friends lives beneath such
a mast. I don't point it out.

I put my phone in flight mode whenever I'm
not using it. Turn off my router at night.

A shudder goes through me each time I see
someone hold up their phone to their ear.

Children with iPads in their strollers.

89

The rays from the screens, from the routers,
do I really feel them?

These entirely invisible, but wholly indisputable
rays passing through us.

Rays nobody can stop, and nobody wants to.

After all, they bring images to our screens.

<u>15:08</u>

Strange
Now that the pain is gone
I no longer remember it —

Plants perceive without images, but photosynthesis requires light-sensitive cells.

Do trees share images with each other underground through the fungal network?

Photoshopped portraits of two-headed deer in Fukushima.

Pictures of a woman whose fillings exploded in a pressure chamber. Whose scars hardened like cement in a CT scan.

90

An X-ray of a man whose bones became brittle as glass after a single dose of steroids.

A deepfake video of a uterus that turns inside out to reveal Putin's talking face.

The tapestry arrived in a truck today. Woven, rolled up, and ready to be hung.

I perceive its spread from
the centre of my body
in every direction

The glands swell in my groin
then under my arms & on my neck

My mother brings hypnosis
The doctor brings drops of opium

It is the latter that gives me back
the vivid dreams of childhood

90

I see myself transform from within
& wake up on the outside of pain
in a body made of gears & cogwheels

I feel the soul detach from the flesh
and begin its journey —

15:26

I see the world as a single
vast length of fabric
weaving & unravelling perpetually

I've only seen a small section because I don't
have a floor big enough to unroll it.

I've finished the tapestry without figuring out
what I want. I am still the wavering Penelope.

Love blinks like a cursor.

I see William's peach-cheeks, his curly hair,
and I think: what now?

Is it this blinking love that's meant to hold
it all together?

Is it the genes' desire to become material? Is it
the material's desire to express meaning?

I tell William: 'I need more time.'

'I am Ada. I'm working on an algorithm of
the nervous system.'

After my death I appear
& disappear like a weft
behind the warp

Now I ask Charles to leave
the operation of his business to me

Now he blankly refuses my proposal

Now the servant rolls a shiny cabinet
of bolts & cogs into Charles's parlours

Now Dickens reads aloud at my deathbed

91 Now I pawn my jewellery

Now I go to the racetrack
& lose everything I wager

15:46

Now I am back at the garment factory

My mother is shown brocades
& the factory owner lowers his voice

A dream of escaping from an unlocked prison.

You were always free to leave, but everywhere there were signs with warnings and advice and guards chasing after me to convince me to stay.

Does William exist outside the prison as well? Can I encounter him there as a free person?

I love him in slow motion and in my sleep.

And yet — the feeling that if he were to break up, I would be the first to get up and grab my coat.

Your father — he says

— raged against these machines

before the House of Lords

He spoke in defence of the Luddites!

The factory owner gives me a sharp look

as if he believes

he could drill holes in my body

out of which my dead father would spill

Is that so — I counter

— that I did not know

& add loudly so my mother can hear —

My admiration for these machines is great

They do not lose a thread

or break a pattern

They can do the work of humans

better faster & without wages

They know no difference between night & day

Their minds are not contorted by love

They do not long for sleep at night

<u>16:15</u>

Now I sit down & write
a letter to my father —

Father was it sympathy for the wretched
or fear of the machines
that bound you to the Luddites

Or was it because they too
were married to fiction?

Pray believe me
Your Ada

93

He does not respond

Probably because he is deceased
or because my mother discards his letters

<u>16:24</u>

Now I pull the fabric aside
& look at my father

Same nose as mine
The same cleft chin

A hint of pink just beneath
the outermost colour of his cheeks

A darker hue where his beard
will soon break through

Both nuances give his face
a wistful synergy
like a bud which will unfurl
its soft petals any minute now

94   I did not know him
but I know that longing

I admit that when I lived
I showed my mother & him
a cold anger

But now that the rage is gone
I no longer remember it —

I remember every time
I turned away from my mother
my father came forth & vice versa

An amulet clasps a lock of my
father's hair
in my mother's dresser

A woman speaks with my mother's voice
in my father's poems

I am Ada

The one who stays
& the one who leaves

The two of them

I carry the strictest
admiration for mathematics
as a language for invisible connections
between things

& the greatest elation
over all that is living

96

PART 7 | THE HYPERLOOM

It's a piece of silk fabric which convinces Google
that they need to build an image-search algorithm.

Gossamer chiffon with palm-leaf print. Semi-sheer,
so it reveals what it obscures. Designed and
fashioned into a dress by Versace and worn to
the Grammy Awards in 2000 by Jennifer Lopez.

The most googled piece of fabric of its time, the
image everyone wants to see.

J-Lo+green+dress, Lopez+green+Versace+dress.

William has left.

He asked me to say that I wanted him.

I couldn't.

Is it over?

It's up to me.

I don't know.

In the year 2000, the computer can read and search text, but it cannot yet see. It blindly offers up whatever images appear in connection with the search words.

How do you get a search engine to search through images consisting of hundreds of thousands of tiny coloured dots? How do you build a loom capable of seeing the image it weaves?

To enable the search engine to see the content of an image, Google sets to work developing neural networks, training them and making them deeper.

Neural networks make it possible to use machines for work we had thought reserved for humans: image analysis, data analysis, assessments, decisions, text generation. More jobs can be abolished.

Didn't fall sleep until four, had to get up
at six to unveil the tapestry without him.

Figures approached me and introduced
themselves with names I recognised.

Admired my reflection in shop windows on the
way home, my face felt firmer than it has done
in a long time, maybe since I was a child.

My cheeks feel like they've been cleansed,
almost shaven.

I walk through the city, glowing. My scars
gleam in car window passe-partouts.

Sunshine over Nørrebro, the walls surrounding
construction sites suddenly translucent.

The chef at Running Sushi on Hillerødgade
stirs a big wooden vat of rice, I watch through
the window from the street.

The word 'text' comes from the Latin *textus*,
which means textile. Like 'tissue', it stems from
texere, to weave.

The internet gave us hypertext with links
interconnecting texts. Hypertext unravels the
threads of a text and connects them across
textiles, inter-net.

Neural networks allow not only text, but also
image matter to become 'hyper'.

Our screens become hyper-fast electronic textiles.
Billions of images are interwoven and unravelled
following infinitely duplicable pixel patterns.

Random pixels, too many to form an image,
fade to black-and-white, slip through an
algorithm and emerge as a sound, a tingle,
a breath.

A black plait against a lavender jacket,
a lopsided grin beneath a bike helmet.

Tiny electric currents pass from the touchpad
to my fingers when the computer is charging.

Want to draw 10 or 20 new works today,
just sketches.

Think of William's soft body and make   100
it grainy.

Why must we be pale and pawned?

Why don't I make a wonderful little film
every day?

Oh, to have seen so-and-so dancing on
their own.

We may imagine it is Penelope weaving and unravelling
the textiles of our screens. Odysseus has not
returned home from his quest. Penelope is still at her
loom, weaving during the day and unravelling at night.
Never a dull moment. Days and nights accelerate to
an almost imperceptible flicker. She no longer has
time to sleep, so she has her marriage bed converted
into a bigger, faster three-dimensional loom.
It weaves images remotely, out of invisible rays.

An egg, runny as snot and warm as a
human being. Boiling by its own heat,
the skin of a child.

Have played guitar all weekend, my
fingertips now tender as sunshine.

The melatonin pills give a groggy state of
happiness. I rub the soles of my feet together
under the blankets.

Is the apartment mine now? Or is it on
holiday?

These morning hours I have missed out on
too often, the mist across the green, the
leaves glistening with dreams.

Cold dew covers my love's body when it wakes.

Need to get myself regular access to nature,
something breathtaking, something simple.

A bird flies into the window and drops into
the bushes. Two pins in a loaf of bread,
pebbles in the wheat.

In the city, pigeons are as grey as the asphalt.

The images that Penelope weaves and unravels
remotely are connected in a three-dimensional
textile: the 'hypertextile'. Her new loom, the
'hyperloom'.

Unlike computer chips, the hyperloom doesn't shrink
with technological advancement.

On the contrary, the more data we feed it, the
bigger the loom gets. The hyperloom grows from
the size of a classroom to a factory. It expands
to the size of a city, an island, a country.

In the year 2022, the hyperloom is the size
of Europe.

All doors are open and it smells of hookah
pipe from a window.

We need to get to a place where I give and
William receives.

I'm the one who must take risks, invest myself,
dare to fail, be rejected.

Distant manor houses are empty and waiting for us.

A fridge with its door ajar, as if someone inside
it were eavesdropping.

Now the moon-shaped lamps come on at the
alternative healers.

Acupuncture travels like electricity through
the nerves.

Breathe into the groin. Send light out through
the eyes.

Feel the soles of the feet take root.

In 2035, the entire planet.

Penelope at her hyperloom creates tangible change in the world, on our screens and in the fabric of our minds.

In the 2010s and 20s, all major museums digitalise their collections, making them freely accessible online.

Around the year 2030, the museums' images start to change. They become three-dimensional. Disparate times and places are brought together in a porous digital architecture. The collections are now riddled with gaps and voids.

The women at the cafés with drooling babies
in their laps. They talk about the children's
fathers, that none of them take responsibility
when the children wake up at night.

'It's your child too!' shouts one woman to
an imaginary man in the conversation.

Later they talk about sex, and another says:
'One has to be a little generous. He has needs
that I don't and one has to acknowledge that.'

William's tender gaze when he sees me through
the glass door of the café, and when he steps
inside the next moment: that gaze, extinguished.

I worry too much about how I turn his gaze
on and off, and too little about my own,
whether it's on or off.

There won't be room for love if we don't make
space for pain too, I told him, as we walked in
the furthest corner of the cemetery.

The images are moving. Grace Hopper's cartoons mate with the drawings of sundew, hatching a new species of sticky, carnivorous insects. Merian's fat silkworms devour a picture of J-Lo's green dress and pupate in their cocoons. They spin an ethereal thread pre-dyed with a palm tree pattern which the Air Loom intercepts and weaves. The Luddites attack the Air Loom's rays.

103

The hyperloom's three-dimensional textiles are attacked by moths. It's the Original Computer Bug and its descendants, rapidly spreading via the internet and mobile network.

Evening: settling down with a body by my side.

Something packed away and stowed behind a door.

A strange weakness in my feet, and again: the desire to reject in order to become strong.

Must try very hard not to snap at him.

I've been tearing up so easily lately, limp and bloated at the same time, like an old leather football.

The apartment like a barrel I'm rolling downhill in.

The smell of whale glands lingers in the furniture.

A worm of light dances above the blinds.

Big crabs biting from all sides.

I no longer want to walk like the sleepless.
Milky sick and nappy changes.

Wrap a white cloth around my head.

Each mirror, a new light on the holes of my face.

The moth swarms appear in every home with a personal computer. In classrooms, among traders, newspapers, politicians. At space stations, military bases, hospitals.

They surge onwards through cables on the ocean floor. They live in data centre high-rises. They flock around mobile phones and masts: 3G, 5G, 9G. They ride the electromagnetic waves that penetrate the body's cells, nibbling on data in DNA chains.

Wherever the moths go, they bring about massive power cuts, gas pipe explosions and faulty connections in the mobile network. They kill patients with lethal radiation doses and send rockets off course. They deposit billions into the accounts of people at random. They slip inside vote-counting software and elect a river to the Indian parliament. They put arbitrary videos on YouTube's trending list. They turn off every stoplight in Dubai.

The rain in the courtyard and a clarinet
behind a door in the stairwell.

A trickle descending down all the stairwells
I've ever known.

I text William: 'Maybe our cat will be
born tonight, and we can pick it up in
10-12 weeks.'

Aren't we all connected to the people
we'll one day become?

They're out there waiting for us, making
clay pots in a sun-filled room.   105

Therapy 21/6: reach out and pull the doubt aside
as if it were a heavy curtain in front of me.

Look to see what's on the other side.

Out of eternity.

When the Starlink network envelops the world in
a textile of rays thicker than a silkworm's cocoon,
the moths flit back and forth between the network's
satellites and between the satellites and Earth.

When the orbital zone becomes so crowded with
satellites they can be used as LEDs to screen logos
and videos onto the night sky, it is the appetite
of the moth larvae that cause private video chats
to mingle with the ads.

105

The population of digital space grows and grows.
In 2033, leaked biometric passports materialise for
the first time as living, speechless beings.

Space-time folded up like brain convolutions
in the universe, pressed together and kneaded
into crystal or shortcrust pastry.

I hold the pastry in my hand and hear
(as I often do) my future children speak.

The lilies make the lobby insistent.

Their scent presses at my senses like a
five-year-old's fingers on an elevator button,
breaking my heart.

This past week: the sobs in my chest want
to wriggle their way out, slip into my nervous
system and buckle my knees.

And now, a strange chill as though in the cold
storage at the supermarket where I had my first job.

Fluctuating in and out of what is clenched,
then opening.

Love as an intense, nauseating joy.

Simultaneously diving in and holding back.

In the 2040s, when brains can be scanned at molecular level, they start uploading, first from worms, then mice, then monkeys and finally from humans.

They're known as 'living images'.

Ada's Algorithm is back at her desk. She studies the new species, working on an algorithm to counteract moths and digital entropy. She imagines the digital as a decentralised organism capable of bearing fruit, setting roots and cleansing the air. A plant, or at least a nervous system, that is not infected.

Again, she is in a race against time. In digital space, time comes in packs for upload and download. Digital entropy increases with processing power and network connection, and both are growing exponentially.

Loose like coffee, wild.

The first time the ocean floor was
photographed, the diver brought down a
magnesium flash bulb in a diver's bell.

The flickering of the gas stove's flame like
shaking a quilted blanket.

We're all the same, ripped in two.

We all differ in our patches and our lives.

One door slams, and another opens.

The light between the weeping willow's
branches.

Not raking light, but the opposite — omni-light.

Pollen in the water bowl outside the café.

Margarine on bread. A helicopter flew in
front of the sun.

Oligarchs and internet billionaires drift around in the ever-expanding digital space, sucking up knowledge and conspiracy theories. Wherever they go, they run into moths that feed on their memories and reweave them into communal fantasies.

107

The living images have paid to be uploaded, though not to dissolve. They seek refuge in the museums' databases.

They enter through the paintings' windows. Formerly flat subjects open up for them, allowing them to travel from place to place through painted vistas, deeper and deeper into the databases.

I smile in sunshine on my way across the
bridge, wanting always to be the one who
smiles and infects others with my smile.

Want to love William the way you roll up
a rice-paper pancake with too much filling.

Wrap your Velcro straps around me.
Bizarre human body.

I'm bleeding and full of hope.

The universe could fit in a thimble,
if necessary.

The moths follow behind.

IMAGES

Thread Ripper is No. 9 in the series
New Scandinavian Literature
Graphic design by Line-Gry Hørup
Printed and bound by TJ Books in the United
Kingdom, 2022

Cover image: *Ada Lovelace at the Piano*,
painted by Henry Phillips, 1852. Wikimedia;
public domain

This translation was made possible through the
generous support of the Danish Arts Foundation
and Fondation Jan Michalski

Danish Arts
Foundation

FONDATION
JAN MICHALSKI
POUR
L'ÉCRITURE
ET LA
LITTERATURE

A CIP catalogue record for this book is
available from the British Library

ISBN: 978-1-9196092-9-4

Lolli Editions
111 Charterhouse Street
London EC1M 6AW
United Kingdom
www.lollieditions.com

ACKNOWLEDGEMENTS

The Danish text embeds short quotes from
other texts, and the English translation
follows this convention. The works quoted
in this English version are listed here in the
order they appear: Ada Lovelace, 'Note A'
to Luigi Menabrea's 'Sketch of the
Analytical Engine invented by Charles
Babbage'; Robert Bresson, *Notes on the
Cinematograph*, trans. Jonathan Griffin;
Charles Babbage, 'Scribbling Book' Vol.
XV; Ada Lovelace, 'Note A' in letter to
Charles Babbage, 5 July 1843; Ada
Lovelace, letter to Woronzow Greig, 15
November 1844; Arthur Miller at the
Cinema 16 symposium, 'Poetry and the
Film', 28 October 1953; William Blake,
'And did those feet in ancient time',
Milton: A Poem in Two Books; Lord
Byron, speech to the House of Lords, 27
February 1812; J.P. Jacobsen, 'Diary of
an Intelligent Young Man, Part III —
Letters and Jottings', trans. Jennifer
Russell; Itō Hiromi, *Wild Grass on the
Riverbank*, trans. Jeffrey Angles; J.P.
Jacobsen, 'On Movement in the Plant
Kingdom', trans. Jennifer Russell; Roland
Barthes, *Empire of Signs*, trans. Richard
Howard; Grace Hopper archives; Thomas
Edison, Letter to Theodore Puskas, 18
November 1878; Trevor Paglen, 'Invisible
Images (Your Pictures are Looking at You)'.

We thank Tilted Axis Press for their
permission to cite from Itō Hiromi's *Killing
Kanoko / Wild Grass on the Riverbank*,
trans. Jeffrey Angles, on page 67.

Thank you Morten, Lea, David, Liv,
Cæcilie, and Luka.